Great Lies to tell Small Kids

Andy Riley is the author of THE BOOK OF BUNNY SUICIDES and RETURN OF THE BUNNY SUICIDES. He has written for Black Books, Little Britain, Smack The Pony, Trigger Happy TV, Big Train and The Armando Iannucci Shows. He is the co-creator of Hyperdrive, BBC2's new science fiction sitcom, and Radio 4's The 99p Challenge. His weekly cartoon strip, Roasted, runs in the Observer Magazine.

Great Lies to tell Small Kids

Andy Riley

HODDER &
STOUGHTON

First published in Great Britain in 2005 by Hodder and Stoughton
A division of Hodder Headline

The right of Andy Riley to be identified as the Author of the Work has been asserted by him in accordance
with the Copyright, Designs and Patents Act 1988

A Hodder & Stoughton book

19

A CIP catalogue record for this title is available from the British Library

Hardback ISBN 978 0 340 83405 3
Paperback ISBN 978 0 340 83406 0

Printed and bound by CPI Group (UK) Ltd, Croydon, CR0 4YY

Hodder Headline's policy is to use papers that are natural, renewable and recyclable products and made from
wood grown in sustainable forests. The logging and manufacturing processes are expected to conform to the
environmental regulations of the country of origin

Hodder and Stoughton Ltd
A division of Hodder Headline
338 Euston Road
London NW1 3BH

With thanks to:
Polly Faber, Camilla Hornby, Nick Davies
and all at Hodder & Stoughton,
Kevin Cecil, Armando Iannucci

Rain is Jesus's wee-wee

THERE'S NO SUCH THING AS KANGAROOS
THEY'RE JUST MICE STANDING VERY NEAR

MOUSE

"KANGAROO"

WINE

MAKES MUMMY
CLEVER

① "SLALOM"

② "CLASSIC"

③ "THE HOOK"

④ "X-TREME"

⑤ "G-SERIES"

⑥ "LATTICE"

⑦ "CHAIN-LINK"

⑧ "MOEBIUS"

WHEN I WAS YOUR AGE WEETABIX CAME IN EIGHT DIFFERENT SHAPES

POLICEMEN GROW FROM HELMETS IN A SINGLE NIGHT ∿

IT'S UNLUCKY <u>NOT</u> TO NAME EVERY ANT YOU SEE

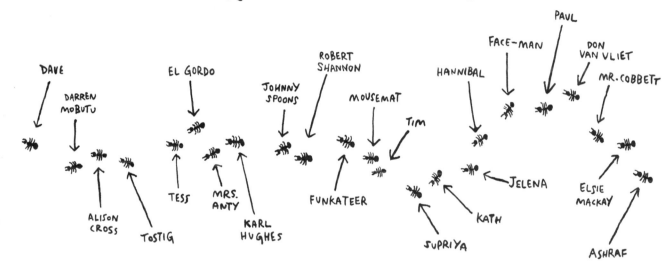

DAVE

DARREN MOBUTU

EL GORDO

ROBERT SHANNON

JOHNNY SPOONS

MOUSEMAT

TIM

HANNIBAL

FACE-MAN

PAUL

DON VAN VLIET

MR.COBBETT

TESS

MRS. ANTY

FUNKATEER

JELENA

ELSIE MACKAY

ALISON CROSS

TOSTIG

KARL HUGHES

KATH

SUPRIYA

ASHRAF

FOR YOUR WHOLE LIFE

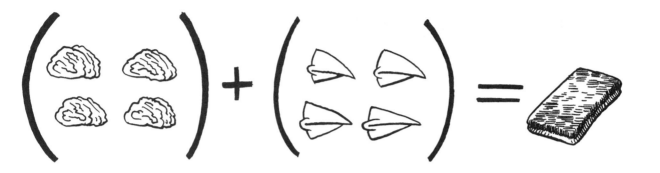

IT TAKES THE BRAINS AND
BEAKS OF FOUR REAL PENGUINS
TO MAKE ONE PENGUIN
BISCUIT

PRECIPITATION

CONDENSATION

EVAPORATION

TRIBUTARY

OX-BOW LAKE

STREAM

RIVER

DELTA

OCEAN

WHEN THEY TEACH YOU THE WATER CYCLE AT SCHOOL, MAKE SURE YOU REMEMBER THE BIT ABOUT **OX-BOW LAKES**. YOU'LL COME ACROSS THEM A **LOT** IN LATER LIFE.

* A SLICE OF CHEESE WILL PLAY A SHORT FILM ABOUT COWS

STRICTLY SPEAKING, THE TOMATO
IS NOT A VEGETABLE

IT'S REALLY A KIND OF DOLPHIN

THE CAN OPENER WAS
INVENTED 98 YEARS
BEFORE THE CAN

ONE IN TEN FISH ARE AFRAID OF WATER

LIONS CARRY BARCODE SCANNERS

THEY RUN THEM OVER ZEBRAS TO CHECK HOW
MUCH THEY COST BEFORE THEY EAT THEM

MEN DON'T GO BALD NATURALLY

THEY JUST LIKE GETTING THEIR HAIR CUT THAT WAY

the victorians forgot to have the year 1862

› the error went unnoticed for more than a century
› the year was finally held between 1995 and 1996

MICE COLLECT YOUR DANDRUFF
AND EAT IT AS CORNFLAKES

THIS SQUARE HAS A SECRET
FIFTH SIDE WHICH YOU WILL
ONLY SEE IF YOU STARE
AT IT FOR A VERY VERY
VERY LONG TIME

SCATTER DRAWING PINS NEXT TO AN ANTS' NEST
THEN WAIT TILL IT RAINS
THEY'LL PICK THEM UP AND USE THEM AS UMBRELLAS

BAR CODES WERE SIMPLER IN THE OLD DAYS

CLOWNS MELT AT 29°C

THE TOOTH FAIRY ONCE WENT TO GET ONE OF DRACULA'S FANGS BUT DRACULA'S CASTLE WAS REALLY DARK SO SHE CUT HERSELF ON THE FANG BY MISTAKE AND EVER SINCE THEN SHE'S BEEN A BLOOD-SUCKING VAMPIRE TOOTH FAIRY.

ANYWAY, GOODNIGHT

THAT WORD DAD
USES SOMETIMES

IT MEANS "PLEASE"

USE IT IN SCHOOL
AND AT THE SHOPS

MUGS ARE JUST CUPS WHO'VE BEEN TO THE GYM

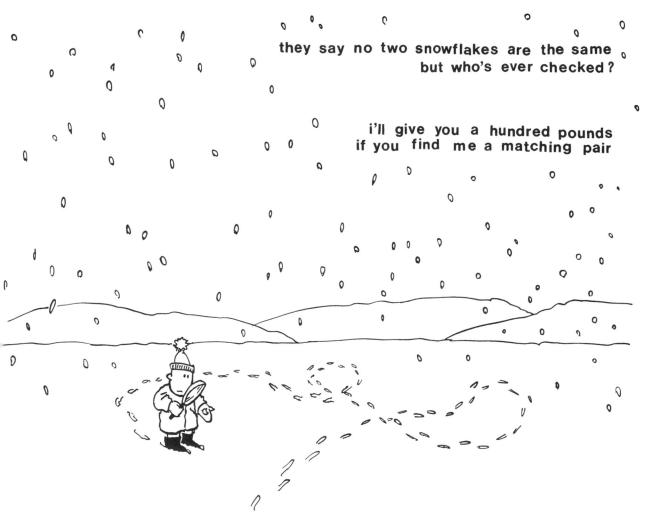

penguins spend a lot of time wondering why pixar have never made a film about them

GODZILLA HAS EVERY FRIDAY OFF

ALL WIND IS MADE BY WIND FARMS

BEWARE OF GUITARS

A SMALL HAIRY
PRIMATE CALLED
A "WARRIS"
LIVES INSIDE
EVERY ONE

THEY LIVE ON
A DIET OF
HUMAN FINGERS

IF YOU GRAB THE EDGE
OF YOUR CHAIR AND
PULL AS HARD AS YOU
CAN YOU'LL LIFT YOURSELF
INTO THE AIR

IT WAS GRANDAD WHO BURIED ALL YOUR BARNEY VIDEOS

NOT US

PUBS HAVE SPECIAL
MAGNETS WHICH
DRAG DAD IN BY
HIS METAL FILLINGS

HE HAS NO CHOICE

THERE USED TO BE A SHIP IN THAT BOTTLE
BUT IT SANK

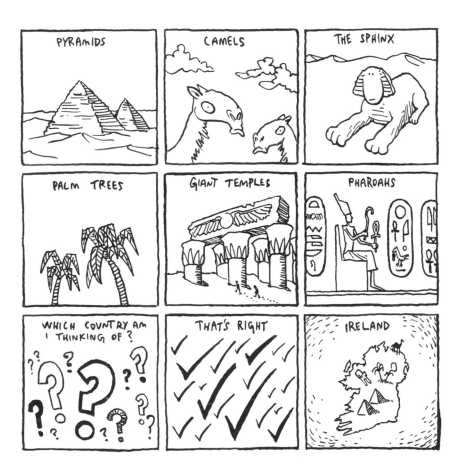

YOUR DAD IS REALLY A YETI
HE SHAVES HIS ENTIRE BODY EVERY MORNING

before

after

"JACK"

CAPTAIN JACK WENDOVER (1715-1763) LOST MORE BODY PARTS THAN ANY OTHER PIRATE IN HISTORY

TWO IN EVERY FORTY THOUSAND
CARS LEAVE THE FACTORY
AS "SIAMESE CARS"

IF THEY SHARE AN AXLE
THEY CAN NEVER BE SEPARATED

ONE IN EIGHT EARTHWORMS HAVE PIERCINGS
ONE IN TWENTY HAVE TATTOOS

MOST BIRDS WEAR PARACHUTES IN CASE THEY SUDDENLY FORGET HOW TO FLY ↶↷

eggs talk to each other after you shut the fridge door

THE WILD WEST WAS ONLY
TEN BY EIGHT FEET WIDE

If you ring the number of a house where you used to live you can talk to THE PAST VERSION OF YOURSELF

Never tell the THE PAST VERSION OF YOURSELF who is calling

NOTE: anyone who rings you and says 'sorry, wrong number' is almost certainly you from the future

WE'LL GIVE YOU A PONY IF YOU CLEAN THE CAR

orange-hatted witches
always forget to
read road signs

KEEP A CHICKEN NUGGET IN A SHOE BOX, LEAVE IT SOME
WATER AND CORN, AND SOON IT WILL GROW INTO A LIVE CHICKEN

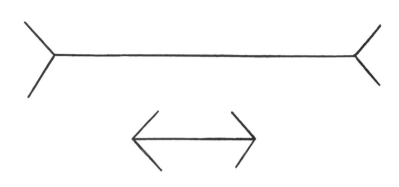

LOOK AT THE TWO HORIZONTAL
LINES ON THIS PAGE. WHICH
ONE IS LONGER?

THE CORRECT ANSWER IS
NEITHER. IF YOU THINK
THE TOP ONE IS LONGER THAT'S
JUST AN OPTICAL ILLUSION.

SAY A PRAYER BEFORE YOU GO TO BED

THEN OPEN THE WINDOW AND MAKE A RABBIT SNARE

BY MORNING YOU'LL HAVE CAUGHT A **REAL ANGEL** TO KEEP AS A PET !!

the statue of liberty switches hands when her torch arm gets tired
she only does it when no-one's looking

1951

1977

1998

the next time should be in about twelve years

WHEN YOU REACH
TWELVE OR SO, YOU WILL
GROW PUBIC HAIR AND
YOUR SKIN MAY GET SPOTTY

AND YOUR NOSE
WILL GROW TINY,
SHARP RETRACTABLE
TEETH CALLED
"DENTICLES"

YOUR DAD IS A SUPER-HERO

>He was bitten by a radioactive MAN, giving him all the powers of a MAN

>His super-hero name is 'MAN-MAN'

>His super-hero costume is jeans and a shirt from Gap

>His arch-nemesis is called 'All The Stuff That Needs Doing'

>Thrill to his exploits!

Q: WHERE DO BATTERIES GET THEIR POWER FROM?

A: TINY PEDALLING MICE

if you saw the queen split open
you'd see she's full of swans

IF YOU STICK YOUR HAND DOWN THE TOILET

IT COMES OUT OF A TOILET IN CHINA

TRY WAVING

SPRINKLE SAND
OUTSIDE AN ANTS' NEST

THEN LAY COTTON BUDS AND
ASSORTED WASHERS ON THE SAND

IN THE MORNING YOU WILL HAVE
YOUR OWN INSECT 'MUSCLE BEACH'

THAT ROAD SIGN MEANS
"BE VERY QUIET
IN THE CAR"

EVERY JUNE, SCOTLAND IS
TOWED 1000 MILES SOUTH
SO IT CAN HAVE A SUMMER

ONLY 10% OF PEOPLE IN
SCOTLAND KNOW THIS

IF YOU UTTER THE TRIGGER WORD "BADMINTON"
TO YOUR GRANDMA

HER ORIGINAL PROGRAMMING WILL ACTIVATE
AND SHE WILL KILL ALL HUMANS

THE BEST COMPUTERS IN THE WORLD CAN BEAT ANYONE AT HUNGRY HUNGRY HIPPOS

EVEN RUSSIAN GRANDMASTERS

FATHER CHRISTMAS IS HIDING IN THE
PAKISTAN / AFGHANISTAN BORDER REGION,
NEVER SLEEPING IN THE SAME PLACE FOR
TWO NIGHTS RUNNING

HE'S ON THE CIA's TEN MOST WANTED LIST

SOME PEOPLE SAY DELTA
FORCE HAVE ALREADY KILLED
HIM

THEY DIDN'T STOP DAD FROM DRIVING
HE'S JUST GIVING HIS ARMS A REST

FOR TWO YEARS

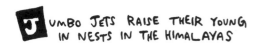**J**UMBO JETS RAISE THEIR YOUNG IN NESTS IN THE HIMALAYAS

THE PARENTS FLY UP TO 3000 MILES TO GATHER NOURISHMENT FOR THE FAST-GROWING "JUMBLETS"

IT'S COMPLETELY IMPOSSIBLE TO
TOUCH YOUR OWN NOSE SO
DON'T EVEN TRY

CLOWNS ARE MADE PURELY
FROM THE CHEMICAL ELEMENT
"CLOWN" (SYMBOL Cw,
ATOMIC WEIGHT 15)

THIS IS AN ATOM OF
CLOWN MAGNIFIED
3,000,000 TIMES

HAMBURGERS IN THE WILD LIVE IN DESERT COLONIES

THEY HIDE UNDER ROCKY OVERHANGS TO AVOID COOKING
THEMSELVES IN THE HEAT OF THE DAY

LEAVE A FEW BOXES OF MATCHES AND SOME DRAWING PINS OUTSIDE AN ANTS' NEST

BY THE NEXT MORNING THEY'LL HAVE SET UP A RICKSHAW BUSINESS FOR SNAILS

THEY'RE NATURAL ENTREPRENEURS, ARE ANTS

WHEN SOMEONE SHAVES OFF A BEARD
IT GOES TO BEARD HEAVEN

ALL BALLOONS HAVE A REFLECTION OF A WINDOW IN THEM *EVEN WHEN THERE IS NO WINDOW NEARBY*

people who wear scarves

are just trying to hide the fact that they've got heads but no necks

THE FASTEST RECORDED 100 METRE
TIME IS 4.8 SECONDS BY MIGUEL
PIÑON IN THE 2000 OLYMPICS

HIS MEDAL WAS LATER CONFISCATED AFTER
A RANDOM TEST SHOWED UP AN ILLEGAL
NUMBER OF LEGS

> CAT POOs ARE WORTH £300 EACH
> COLLECT THEM WITH TONGS
> WHEN YOU'VE GOT FIFTY, TAKE THEM TO THE
  POST OFFICE AND CLAIM YOUR MONEY

YOU KNOW MY MUG IN THE KITCHEN? THE ONE THAT SAYS

THERE ARE
ONLY THREE
IN EXISTENCE

THEY ARE
AWARDED
JUST ONCE
EVERY 100
YEARS

I KNOW YOU DIDN'T SEE ANY GHOSTS WHEN WE VISITED THE CASTLE

T HAT'S BECAUSE THEY WERE ALL ON THEIR FAG BREAK

WE DIDN'T HAVE I-PODS WHEN I WAS YOUR AGE

SO WE ALL HAD 20 PIECE MARCHING BANDS
WITH 10,000 SONGS MEMORISED

if you spin round really fast and then stop your face will skid round to the back of your head

IF YOU BREAK THE LAW OF GRAVITY THE PENALTY IS HANGING

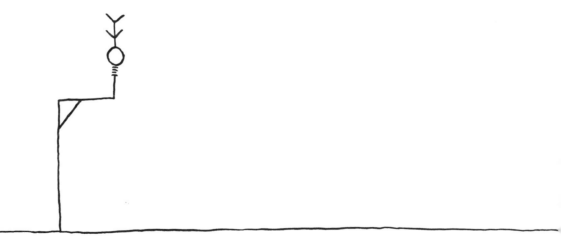

sometimes a daddy mole and a mummy giraffe have babies

though it's generally discouraged

THERE:

I'VE
DONE
YOU
AS
SPIDERMAN

THE END

NOW GO AND PLAY NICELY
AND NEVER EVER TELL FIBS